Stop Fent

Parent and School Guide to Understanding & Addressing the Fentanyl Epidemic With Their Youth

Armand King

Edited by C.H. Gorrie

Ariginal One LLC
Walk With Me Impact Media & Education

- Overdose, not per driving
  Protection
  Law
- good samartan
  Law

Table of Contents

The Author's Connection

As I reflect on my life, I can't help but be passionate about the dangers of drug addiction. I have witnessed the devastating impact it has on families and communities. I know this firsthand, having been a part of the illegal drug trade and struggling with addiction myself for many years. But now, I am grateful for my life and the opportunity to make a difference. For the past 12 years, I have been actively helping people in my community and abroad to break free from toxic lifestyles and activities. I have been on the front lines, doing everything I can to save lives and offer hope to those who have lost it.

Regarding drugs and the loss of life, the past few years have been some of the toughest I have ever faced. In 2017, one of my closest friends died as a result of Fentanyl. His name was Wiliam Waggoner III. I thought it couldn't get any worse, but in the past two years, I have lost nearly two dozen close friends to this deadly drug. It breaks my heart to see so many young lives cut short by this drug.

That's why I am using my experience and energy to speak out about the deadly impact of Fentanyl. I am urging everyone to join me in this fight, especially those who have influence over the youth. We need to get this message out as quickly as possible and spread it wide and far. Let's work together to raise awareness about the dangers of Fentanyl and offer hope to those struggling with addiction.

— Armand Lawrich King

"Protect Our Youth"

Fentanyl, oh Fentanyl
A deadly drug, a living hell
It preys on the young, the old, the strong
And leaves behind a mournful song

Our youth, so bright, so full of dreams
But Fentanyl tears at the seams
Of families, schools, and communities
Leaving behind only pain and unease

We must educate, we must inform
We must prevent before addictions are born
Into the trap of addiction, so deep
Where life and death, they interweave

Let us speak with love, with care
And help our youth become aware
Of the danger lurking in plain sight
So they can choose a path that's right

Fentanyl, oh Fentanyl
We must stop its deadly spell
Let's work together, hand in hand
And protect our youth across the land.

I dedicate this book to my childhood friend and brother, William Waggoner III, who was the first person I loved that fell victim to Fentanyl.

Sunrise
February 10, 1981

Sunset
June 27, 2017

Forever in Our Hearts
William Waggoner 3rd

Fentanyl Awareness

As a youth advocate who has experienced the devastating effects of Fentanyl firsthand, I cannot stress enough the importance of educating our youth about the dangers of this deadly drug. In my years of working with young people, I have seen the devastating consequences of Fentanyl use and the tragic loss of lives that can result. This section on Fentanyl awareness is written with the aim of providing parents, educators, and anyone working with young people with the information they need to help understand this deadly epidemic.

What Is It?

Fentanyl is a powerful synthetic opioid drug that is similar to morphine but is up to 50-100 times more potent. It is prescribed by doctors to treat severe pain in patients who have developed a tolerance to other pain medications. However, Fentanyl is also used illicitly as a recreational drug because of its euphoric effects.

Fentanyl is a dangerous drug that can cause serious harm and even death, particularly when it is used improperly or abused. One of the main risks of Fentanyl use is overdose, which can occur when a person takes too much of the drug, uses it in a way that is not intended, or mixes it with other drugs or alcohol. Fentanyl overdose can cause respiratory depression, which means that it causes a person's breathing to slow down or stop, which can lead to brain damage or death.

Fentanyl is a growing concern in many countries, including the United States, where it has been linked to a significant increase in drug overdoses deaths in recent years. It is important for individuals to be aware of the risks associated with Fentanyl use, particularly if they are taking it for medical purposes or are at risk of using it recreationally. It is also important for individuals to seek help if they or someone they know is struggling with addiction to Fentanyl or other opioids.

How Much Can Be Lethal?

The amount of Fentanyl that can be lethal can vary depending on several factors, including a person's tolerance to the drug, their weight, and the purity of the Fentanyl they are using. Fentanyl is an extremely potent drug, and even small amounts can be lethal.

According to the US Drug Enforcement Administration (DEA), the lethal dose of Fentanyl for an average-sized adult is estimated to be about 2 milligrams. However, even a much smaller amount can be fatal if the drug is highly potent or if a person is not tolerant to its effects.

It's important to note that Fentanyl is a dangerous drug that can cause serious harm even at lower doses, particularly when it is used improperly or abused. The risk of overdose and death is very high with Fentanyl use, especially when it is combined with other substances like alcohol or other opioids. If you or someone you know is struggling with addiction to Fentanyl or other drugs, it is important to seek help from a medical professional or a drug treatment program.

The Statistics

Fentanyl has been implicated in countless cases of overdose and death, especially when used recklessly or abused. Here are some statistics on Fentanyl-related deaths for several major countries around the globe, as of 2021:

1. **United States:** Fentanyl is a leading cause of drug overdose deaths in the United States, with over 36,000 deaths attributed to synthetic opioids like Fentanyl in 2019. (Source: National Institute on Drug Abuse)
2. **Canada:** Fentanyl-related deaths have been increasing rapidly in Canada in recent years, with over 6,000 deaths attributed to synthetic opioids like Fentanyl in 2018. (Source: Canadian Institute for Health Information)
3. **United Kingdom:** Fentanyl-related deaths in the United Kingdom have been increasing in recent years, with 61 deaths attributed to Fentanyl in 2018. (Source: Office for National Statistics)
4. **Australia:** Fentanyl-related deaths in Australia have also been increasing in recent years, with

204 deaths attributed to Fentanyl in 2018.
(Source: Australian Bureau of Statistics)

It's important to note that these statistics may not capture the full scope of the Fentanyl epidemic, as Fentanyl use and overdose deaths can often go unreported or undetected. Additionally, the statistics may vary depending on how deaths related to Fentanyl are classified and reported in different countries.

Methods of Delivery

As the deadly opioid crisis continues to sweep the globe, Fentanyl has become one of the most commonly used opioids in the United States and beyond. What's even more alarming is that it's increasingly being mixed with other substances, making it difficult to detect and leading to a surge in overdoses. This is especially concerning for parents and school staff, who may not be aware of the various ways in which Fentanyl is being used unknowingly, including lacing other drugs, counterfeit pills, and even being disguised as other substances. It's more important than ever to be informed and educated on the dangers of Fentanyl to protect our youth.

The Harsh Reality of Fentanyl: A Deadly Game of Russian Roulette

The current state of drug use is like playing Russian Roulette with your life, as the stakes are now higher than ever. None of my friends who died from Fentanyl knew they were taking it. Although some people intentionally use Fentanyl to get high, those in my personal circle did not have any intentions of using the drug. I avoid using the term "Fentanyl overdose" in this situation, as the individuals were not aware of what they were taking—it was more like poisoning. Even drug dealers who sell Fentanyl may not know they have it in their possession, making it even more dangerous for users.

It's concerning that individuals who use drugs, especially youth, may purchase from someone they know and trust, not realizing that the person is unaware of what they are doing or selling. I have known of family members unknowingly selling Fentanyl to another family member, leading to an overdose, with the dealer not even realizing what they had.

Illegal Fentanyl Distribution Methods

1. **Drug trafficking**: Fentanyl is often trafficked illegally into the country from other countries or manufactured domestically in clandestine labs. Traffickers may distribute the drug through various channels, such as street dealers or online marketplaces.
2. **Counterfeit pills:** Fentanyl may be added to counterfeit pills that are made to look like prescription benzodiazepines or opioids, such as Xanax, Percocet, oxycodone, or hydrocodone. These pills are often sold on the

street and may be difficult for users to distinguish from genuine medications.

3. **Cutting agents:** Fentanyl may be added as a cutting agent to other drugs, such as heroin or cocaine, to increase their potency. Users may be unaware that they are consuming Fentanyl and are at a higher risk of overdose.

4. **Online sales:** Fentanyl is also being distributed through online marketplaces, such as the dark web, where buyers and sellers can remain anonymous, and transactions can be difficult to track.

It's important to note that Fentanyl is an extremely potent and dangerous drug, and its use can have serious health consequences. Even if the use does not result in death, the person taking the drug may suffer long-term health consequences, such as brain damage or organ failure, that can significantly impact their quality of life. Additionally, the trauma of experiencing a drug overdose can have lasting psychological effects on the user and their loved ones.

The illegal distribution and use of Fentanyl is a major public health concern, and efforts are being made to curb its distribution and provide education and prevention efforts to reduce the harms associated with the drug.

There are five primary ways that people end up taking Fentanyl, which I'll discuss in further detail below.

Pills

The opioid crisis has been exacerbated by the widespread production and distribution of counterfeit pills. Counterfeit pills are illegally manufactured and sold on the street and are made to look like prescription medications, such as Xanax, Percocet, oxycodone, or hydrocodone. These counterfeit pills are made using pill presses and often contain Fentanyl. Because the counterfeit pills look like prescription medications, users may mistakenly believe that they are taking a genuine medication and may not realize that the pills contain Fentanyl.

The issue with counterfeit pills containing Fentanyl is that the amount of Fentanyl in the pill can be highly variable and difficult to predict. Even a small amount of Fentanyl can be lethal, and users may accidentally take a deadly dose of the drug. This is a major concern because Fentanyl is much more potent than other opioids, and its effects are much stronger and can last much longer. In addition, Fentanyl can cause respiratory depression, which can be life-threatening.

As a result, it's important for people to be aware of the dangers of counterfeit pills and to avoid taking any medications that were not prescribed to them by a doctor. It's also important for people to be aware of the signs of a Fentanyl overdose, which can include slowed breathing, extreme drowsiness, and unresponsiveness. If someone suspects they or someone else has taken a counterfeit pill or has overdosed on Fentanyl, they should seek immediate medical attention by calling 911 or going to the nearest emergency room.

Cocaine

Cutting agents are substances that are added to drugs to increase their volume or weight, making them more profitable for drug dealers. Fentanyl may be added as a cutting agent to other drugs, such as heroin or cocaine, to increase their potency. This means that even a small amount of Fentanyl added to another drug can significantly increase the drug's effects.

The danger with Fentanyl being added as a cutting agent is that it can be difficult for users to know that they are consuming Fentanyl, which is more powerful than many other opioids. Users may believe that they are taking a less potent drug, such as heroin or cocaine, and may take a dose that they believe is safe. However, the addition of even a small amount of Fentanyl can greatly increase the risk of overdose.

Compared to other opioids, Fentanyl is remarkably potent, and its consumption can result in life-threatening respiratory depression. Moreover, Fentanyl's ability to penetrate the skin makes it an imminent threat to all individuals who come in contact with the drug, including medical and law enforcement personnel.

To reduce the risk of overdose, it's important for people to be aware of the potential for Fentanyl to be added as a cutting agent to other drugs. It's also important to avoid using any drugs that were not prescribed to them by a doctor, and to seek medical attention if they suspect that they or someone else has overdosed on Fentanyl or another drug. Finally, people who are struggling with substance abuse should seek help from a qualified healthcare professional or addiction treatment center.

Vape

Fentanyl has been found in some counterfeit vaping devices, although it is not a common occurrence. Counterfeit vaping devices are often made using low-quality materials and may not meet safety standards, making them potentially dangerous to users. In some cases, counterfeit vaping devices may contain other substances, such as synthetic cannabinoids or Fentanyl, that are not typically found in legitimate vaping products.

The addition of Fentanyl to counterfeit vaping devices is a concern and youth should be aware of this as they are the ones most at risk of purchasing due to age restrictions. The effects of vaping Fentanyl can be very strong and can last much longer than other forms of Fentanyl use, such as injection or snorting.

To reduce the risk of exposure to Fentanyl or other harmful substances, it's important to avoid using counterfeit vaping devices or any products that were not obtained from a reputable and trustworthy source.

Cannabis

It is possible for Fentanyl to be found in cannabis, although it is not a common occurrence. Fentanyl is an opioid drug that is typically used as a pain medication, and it is not typically found in cannabis, which is a plant-based substance.

However, the illegal drug market is unregulated, and some drug dealers may add Fentanyl to cannabis to increase its potency and create a more intense high.

To reduce the risk of exposure to Fentanyl or other harmful substances, it's important to avoid using cannabis or any other drugs that were not obtained from a reputable and trustworthy source. If someone suspects that they or someone else has consumed cannabis that may be laced with Fentanyl or another harmful substance, they should seek immediate medical attention by calling 911 or going to the nearest emergency room.

Direct

Yes, some people use Fentanyl directly to get high. As previously discussed, Fentanyl is a potent opioid that can produce intense feelings of euphoria, relaxation, and pain relief, making it a desirable drug for people who are seeking a high. However, using Fentanyl directly for non-medical purposes can be extremely dangerous because it is much more potent than other opioids, and its effects are much stronger and can last much longer.

In addition to pill form, people can use Fentanyl in a variety of other ways, including:

1. **Injection:** Fentanyl can be injected intravenously, often mixed with other drugs or substances, such as heroin or cocaine.
2. **Transdermal patches:** Fentanyl is available in a transdermal patch that can be applied to the skin. The patch releases the drug slowly over time, providing pain relief for up to 72 hours.
3. **Nasal spray:** Fentanyl is available in a nasal spray that can be used to manage breakthrough pain in cancer patients.
4. **Lozenges:** Fentanyl lozenges are designed to be dissolved in the mouth and are used to manage breakthrough pain in cancer patients.
5. **Inhalation:** Fentanyl can be inhaled through smoking or vaporization, although this is less common than other forms of use.

"But Drug Dealers Are Killing Their Customers"

When speaking to young people, I'm often asked a thought-provoking question: "If Fentanyl is so dangerous, why do people sell it?" While there may not be a simple answer to this question, I can share my own experiences and speculations. Each person is unique, and their intentions can vary, particularly when it comes to drug dealing. In my personal experience and through my deep connection to the streets, I have found that most corner drug dealers are unaware of when their drugs are laced with Fentanyl. They may even have a drug on their menu for sale that contains

Fentanyl, but not enough to cause harm in every portion.

This brings us back to the dangerous game of Russian Roulette. It seems unlikely that someone in the business of selling drugs would intentionally kill off their customers for profit. However, in most cases, Fentanyl-laced drugs have passed through the hands of at least three higher-level dealers before reaching the street dealer. At any point in this chain, a greedy and careless individual could have added Fentanyl to the mix.

Not If, But When

It is crucial for parents, schools, and communities to take action in raising awareness about Fentanyl and its deadly consequences. With Fentanyl deaths on the rise, we cannot afford to turn a blind eye and hope for the best. We must arm our youth with knowledge and resources to prevent them from falling victim to this toxic substance. It is not a matter of if, but when, Fentanyl will impact our communities, and we must be proactive in our efforts to prevent further tragedy. Let us work together to educate, protect, and save lives.

Prevention

As a youth advocate who has seen the devastating impact of Fentanyl on young people, I cannot stress enough the importance of prevention and awareness. From my experience, prevention is much more effective than intervention once someone has become addicted. The value of education and awareness cannot be overstated, especially when it comes to a drug as deadly as Fentanyl. In this section, we will discuss the importance of prevention and the strategies that can be used to help our youth avoid the dangers of Fentanyl.

Should Parents Talk to Their Kids About Fentanyl?

From my perspective, parents and guardians represent the first line of defense against the deadly Fentanyl epidemic. As the primary teachers and mentors for their children, they are most familiar with their traits and behaviors. Although children naturally experience mood and habit changes as they grow, parents and guardians generally have a closer watch on them than anyone else. This vigilance can help detect signs of drug use. Additionally, their relationship gives them a position of influence and reach that can be used to warn their children of potential dangers.

It's important for parents to talk to their kids about Fentanyl for several reasons. Fentanyl is a powerful and potentially lethal drug that has been linked to a significant increase in overdose deaths in recent years, particularly among young people. By having an open and honest conversation with their kids about the risks of Fentanyl use, parents can help their kids make more informed decisions about drug use and avoid potentially life-threatening situations.

Here are some reasons why parents should talk to their kids about Fentanyl:

1. **Fentanyl use is on the rise:** Fentanyl use has been increasing rapidly in many countries, including the United States and Canada. It's important for parents to be aware of this trend and to talk to their kids about the risks associated with Fentanyl use.
2. **Fentanyl can be deadly:** Fentanyl is an extremely potent drug that can be lethal even at very low doses. It's important for parents to communicate the serious health risks associated with Fentanyl use, and to encourage their kids to avoid experimenting with drugs altogether.
3. **Kids may not know what they're getting:** Fentanyl can be mixed with other drugs or sold as other drugs, making it difficult to know what you're getting when you use illicit drugs. By talking to their kids about the risks of Fentanyl use, parents can help them make more informed decisions and avoid potentially dangerous situations.
4. **Prevention is key:** One of the most important reasons for parents to talk to their kids about Fentanyl is to prevent drug use before it starts. By having ongoing conversations about drug

use and the risks associated with Fentanyl, parents can help their kids develop a strong sense of self-worth, healthy coping skills, and positive relationships that can protect them from the harms of drug use. It is crucial for parents to have open conversations with their children about the dangers of Fentanyl. The last thing any parent wants is to deny the possibility of their child's risk of drug use and then end up planning their funeral due to an overdose. Though it may sound tough, it's the harsh reality that many parents are facing today. Therefore, parents must not make the mistake of assuming their child would never get involved in drugs and end up regretting it later. Don't be that parent!

It's a worrying trend that some kids rely on their friends for information and guidance, especially when it comes to sensitive and important issues like health and drugs.

The dangers of being misinformed are very real. Without access to accurate and reliable sources of information, young people may end up making poor decisions that could have serious consequences for their health and wellbeing. This is particularly concerning when it comes to taking pills or other contraband from friends, which can put them at risk of overdose, addiction, or other serious health problems.

As a society, it's our responsibility to ensure that young people have access to accurate and age-appropriate information about drugs, health, and other important topics. We need to teach them the skills to critically evaluate information from different sources, and to make informed decisions based on their own values and needs. This will not only help to keep them safe and healthy, but also empower them to become responsible and informed members of their community.

By talking to their kids about Fentanyl, parents can help them stay safe, healthy, and drug-free, and build a trusting and supportive relationship with their children.

Just Say No

As a teenager, it's important to understand that drug use can have serious and potentially life-threatening consequences. One of the most dangerous drugs on the market right now is Fentanyl, a synthetic opioid that can be up to 100 times more powerful than other opioids like morphine or heroin. Fentanyl use has been linked to a sharp increase in drug overdose deaths, particularly among young people.

According to the National Institute on Drug Abuse, there were over 36,000 overdose deaths involving synthetic opioids like Fentanyl in the United States in 2019. While data on Fentanyl-related deaths specifically among teens is limited, there has been a concerning increase in Fentanyl-related deaths among young people in recent years. A study published in the *Journal of Adolescent Health* found that the rate of drug overdose deaths among adolescents aged 15-19 increased by over 19% per year between 2014 and 2018, and that synthetic opioids like Fentanyl were involved in a growing number of these deaths.

It's important to understand that even a small amount of Fentanyl can be lethal, and that there is no way to know for sure what you are getting when you use illicit drugs. Fentanyl can be mixed with other substances or sold as other drugs, making it difficult to identify and potentially deadly. It's never worth the risk to experiment with drugs, particularly in today's environment where even a single use could be fatal.

Saying no to drugs is not always easy, but it's important to prioritize your health and safety over peer pressure or curiosity. There are many resources available to help young people make informed decisions about drug use, including school-based prevention programs, support groups, and drug treatment programs. Remember, your life and health are worth more than a fleeting high, and there are many other ways to have fun and enjoy life without resorting to drugs.

Breaking Down Fentanyl to Kids: Adapting to Different Levels of Understanding

Having conversations with young people about drugs can be challenging, especially since different age groups may have varying levels of knowledge and comprehension. Nevertheless, there are certain essential elements that we can incorporate into these discussions to make them effective and applicable to all age groups. We can start by remembering to use simple language when necessary, start with the basics, be honest, use visuals, reinforce positive behaviors, and encourage open communication.

Elementary School Level

Simplifying the language you use when talking to young children about drugs can be more effective when trying to connect with them. To begin, start with the basics by explaining that drugs are harmful substances that can damage their bodies and minds. Fentanyl, in particular, is a drug that is especially dangerous because it can make you very sick or even stop your breathing, which can be life-threatening. Help them understand the consequences of not being able to breathe, which can be very serious. Even a small amount of Fentanyl can be extremely hazardous, and its use can greatly impact your life and, in severe cases, can lead to death.

It's important to clarify that although Fentanyl is a medicine that you can get from a doctor, Fentanyl is also illegally manufactured and sold on the streets, sometimes as counterfeit pills that are made to look like other prescription medications. It is a type of drug that people use to feel good, but it can be very dangerous and even deadly. It's important to never take drugs that are not prescribed by a doctor or given to you by a trusted adult.

If you ever see Fentanyl or any other drugs, it's important to stay away from them and tell a grown-up that you trust right away. Remember, it's important to always make healthy and safe choices for your body and mind, and that means saying no to drugs.

Middle School Level

When talking to middle schoolers about Fentanyl, it's important to use language they can understand and relate to. One way to help them understand is by sharing real-life stories about the dangers of Fentanyl. Fentanyl is a very potent synthetic opioid drug that can be extremely hazardous to your health. While doctors sometimes prescribe it to treat severe pain, it can also be illegally manufactured and sold on the streets. Fentanyl is so dangerous because even a tiny amount of it can be deadly. That's why it's essential to stay away from this drug and never take it unless it's prescribed by a doctor and taken under their supervision.

When people take Fentanyl, it can make them feel relaxed and euphoric, but it can also slow down their breathing and heart rate, and even cause them to stop breathing. Fentanyl is especially dangerous when it is mixed with other drugs, which can make it even more powerful and unpredictable.

It's important to never take drugs that are not prescribed by a doctor or given to you by a trusted adult. If you or someone you know is struggling with drug addiction, it's important to seek help from a healthcare professional. There are many resources available to help people overcome addiction and stay healthy.

Remember, making healthy and safe choices for your body and mind means saying no to drugs, and never taking any drugs that you are unsure about. By making informed and responsible decisions, you can protect yourself and those around you from the dangers of drug use.

High School Level

For high school-aged youth, it's important to provide more detailed information about Fentanyl, while still using language they can understand. Fentanyl is a synthetic opioid drug that is significantly more potent than other opioids like morphine or heroin. While it can be prescribed by doctors to treat severe pain in cancer patients or others with chronic pain, it's also made and sold illegally on the streets.

The high potency of Fentanyl makes it very dangerous, as even a small amount can lead to an overdose and death. Fentanyl can be found in various forms, including as a powder, a pill, or mixed with other drugs like cocaine or methamphetamine. Because it's often mixed with other drugs, users may not even be aware that they are taking Fentanyl, putting them at an even greater risk. It's important to be aware of the dangers of Fentanyl, and to avoid using it unless it's prescribed by a doctor and taken under their supervision.

Reiterate the potential health and life-threatening effects of Fentanyl, and that it can cause people to stop breathing, even in very small amounts. It is especially dangerous when it is mixed with other drugs, which can make it even more powerful and unpredictable. Overdosing on Fentanyl can be deadly, and many people have died as a result of taking the drug.

While Fentanyl is often used to treat pain, it can also be addictive and lead to substance use disorders. Using Fentanyl or any other drug that is not prescribed by a doctor or given to you by a trusted adult can be very dangerous and can have serious consequences.

Encourage youth to speak up. If you or someone you know is struggling with drug addiction, it's important to seek help from a healthcare professional. There are many resources available to help people overcome addiction and stay healthy.

Remember, making healthy and safe choices for your body and mind means saying no to drugs, and never taking any drugs that you are unsure about. By making informed and responsible decisions, you can protect yourself and those around you from the dangers of drug use, including Fentanyl.

Young College Student

As college students begin their adult life and venture away from home and their support system, it's important to have a conversation about the potential risks of drug and alcohol use. While you may be excited about all the new experiences that college has to offer, it's important to be aware of the dangers of substances like Fentanyl, a highly potent drug that can be incredibly dangerous.

Fentanyl is a synthetic opioid drug that is much more powerful than other types of opioids, like morphine or heroin. Even a very small amount of Fentanyl can be deadly, and it's often used illegally. It can slow down breathing and heart rate and cause people to stop breathing altogether, which can be fatal.

As a young adult, you may feel pressure to try new things and fit in with your peers, but it's crucial that you understand the risks associated with drug use. If you or someone you know is struggling with addiction, it's important to seek professional help. There are many resources available to support you on your journey to recovery.

It's important that you make informed and responsible decisions about drug use. That means saying no to drugs and never taking any substance that you're unsure about. You need to prioritize your health and wellbeing so that you can achieve your goals and dreams without putting yourself in danger.

Remember, your health and safety are our top priority as your parents, and we are here to support you as you navigate this new phase of your life. If you have any questions or concerns, please don't hesitate to reach out to us for help and guidance.

Fentanyl Test Strips

Fentanyl test strips are a type of rapid diagnostic test that can be used to detect the presence of Fentanyl in a sample of drugs. They are paper strips that are coated with antibodies that can bind to Fentanyl or related compounds in a sample. The strips work by dipping them into a solution of the drug, and then waiting a few minutes for the results to appear.

Fentanyl test strips are becoming increasingly popular as a harm reduction tool, particularly among people who use drugs recreationally. The idea is that by testing their drugs for the presence of Fentanyl, users can make more informed decisions about how much to use and how to take the drug more safely. If a test strip indicates the presence of Fentanyl, for example, a user may choose to use a smaller amount or avoid the drug altogether.

The efficiency rate of Fentanyl test strips can vary depending on a number of factors, including the concentration of Fentanyl in the drug sample and the quality of the test strips being used. Some studies have found that test strips can accurately detect the presence of Fentanyl in drug samples, with sensitivity and specificity rates ranging from 86-100% depending on the brand and test conditions.

However, it's important to note that even if a test strip indicates that there is no Fentanyl present in a drug sample, there is still a risk of the drug being contaminated or mixed with other dangerous substances. Test strips are not a foolproof method for ensuring drug safety, and users should always take other harm reduction measures, such as using with a buddy, carrying naloxone, and seeking medical attention if necessary.

Check Off the Box

In conclusion, it is essential for parents and guardians to have open and honest conversations with their children about the dangers of Fentanyl. By doing so, they can provide them with the necessary information and tools to make informed decisions and avoid the potentially fatal consequences of drug use. As the first line of defense, parents and guardians have the power to save their children's lives by educating and warning them about the dangers of Fentanyl and other drugs. Do not leave the drug warning box unchecked.

Intervention

Intervening in a youth's drug addiction can be a difficult and complex process, especially when Fentanyl is involved. As a mentor and advocate for youth, I have seen firsthand the devastating effects of addiction, and the urgent need for effective intervention strategies. This guidebook section aims to provide parents, teachers, and caregivers with practical tips and advice on how to identify the warning signs of drug use and intervene in a way that is supportive, effective, and ultimately lifesaving. Whether you are a concerned parent, teacher, or friend, this section will help to equip you with the tools and knowledge necessary to help prevent youth from falling victim to Fentanyl and other dangerous drugs.

If Your Kid Is Using

If a parent suspects that their child is using harmful drugs, it's important to take action to help them get the support they need. Here are some steps that parents can take:

1. **Start a conversation:** The first step is to talk to your child about your concerns. It's important to approach the conversation in a non-judgmental and supportive way, and to listen to your child's perspective. Ask your child if they are using drugs (and if so, how often), and express your concerns about the potential risks and consequences of drug use.
2. **Seek professional help:** If you suspect that your child is using drugs, it's important to seek

professional help. This could include talking to your child's doctor, a school counselor, or a drug treatment specialist. These professionals can provide guidance and support, and help you develop a plan for addressing the issue.

3. **Provide a safe and supportive environment:** It's important to create a safe and supportive environment for your child to talk about their drug use and get the help they need. This may involve making changes to your home environment, such as removing drugs or drug paraphernalia, and establishing clear rules and boundaries around drug use.

4. **Encourage treatment:** If your child is struggling with drug use, it's important to encourage them to seek treatment. Treatment options may include outpatient counseling, inpatient rehabilitation, or medication-assisted treatment. Encourage your child to participate in treatment and provide support and encouragement throughout the process.

5. **Take care of yourself:** It's important for parents to take care of themselves during this challenging time. This may involve seeking support from friends or family members, attending a support group for parents of children with drug abuse issues, or engaging in self-care activities like exercise or meditation.

It's important for parents to remember that drug addiction is a complex and challenging issue, and that there is no one-size-fits-all solution. By taking a supportive and compassionate approach, seeking professional help, and providing a safe and supportive environment, parents can help their children overcome drug addiction and achieve long-term recovery.

Talk to Them

Talking to your kids about drugs can be an anxiety-inducing and challenging conversation, but it's an important one to have. Here are some tips for overcoming anxiety and fear and having an open and honest conversation with your kids:

1. **Educate yourself:** Before starting the conversation, take some time to educate yourself about drugs and drug use. This can help you feel more confident and prepared to answer your child's questions and concerns.
2. **Focus on facts:** When talking to your child about drugs, focus on the facts and the potential risks and consequences of drug use. Avoid using scare tactics or exaggerating the dangers, as this can undermine your child's trust in you and may not be an effective way to communicate your message.
3. **Be open and non-judgmental:** It's important to approach the conversation in a non-judgmental and supportive way, and to listen to your child's perspective. Avoid lecturing or criticizing, and instead try to create an open and honest dialogue with your child.
4. **Use real-life examples:** Using real-life examples can help your child understand the potential risks and consequences of drug use. This could include stories from the news or

from your own personal experiences or the experiences of people you know.

5. **Emphasize personal responsibility:** It's important to emphasize personal responsibility and the importance of making healthy choices. Encourage your child to be mindful of the potential risks associated with drug use, and to make informed decisions that prioritize their health and well-being.

Talking to your kids about drugs can be a difficult and uncomfortable conversation, but it's important for their health and safety. By taking a supportive and compassionate approach, focusing on the facts, and emphasizing personal responsibility, you can help your child make informed decisions and avoid the potential risks of drug use.

Approaching your child about Fentanyl can be a challenging conversation, but it's an important one to have, especially given the growing number of Fentanyl-related deaths among young people. Here are some methods and talking points that can help:

1. **Start the conversation early:** It's never too early to start talking to your child about drug use, including Fentanyl. Begin the conversation when your child is young and continue to have open and honest conversations as they grow and mature.

2. **Use age-appropriate language:** When talking to younger children, use simple and age-appropriate language to help them understand the potential risks and consequences of drug

use. As they get older, you can use more complex language and provide more detailed information.

3. **Create a safe and supportive environment:** It's important to create a safe and supportive environment for your child to talk about drug use and ask questions. Let your child know that they can come to you with any concerns or questions they may have, and that you are there to support them.

4. **Focus on the facts:** When talking to your child about Fentanyl, focus on the facts and the potential risks and consequences of using the drug. Use real-life examples and emphasize the importance of making healthy choices.

5. **Emphasize personal responsibility:** It's important to emphasize personal responsibility and the importance of making informed decisions. Encourage your child to make informed decisions and to prioritize their health and well-being.

Some talking points that parents can use when talking to their child about Fentanyl include:

- What Fentanyl is and why it is so dangerous
- The potential risks and consequences of using Fentanyl, including overdose and death
- How to recognize the signs of Fentanyl use in oneself or others
- The importance of seeking professional help for drug addiction
- Strategies for coping with stress and anxiety without using drugs

Remember, the key to talking to your child about Fentanyl is to create a safe and supportive environment, use age-appropriate language and information, and encourage open and honest communication. By having ongoing conversations with your child, you can help them make informed decisions and stay safe and healthy. Additionally, parents can encourage their child to use harm reduction strategies like Fentanyl test strips, which can detect the presence of Fentanyl in a drug sample and allow users to take appropriate precautions to avoid potentially lethal doses.

Seek Treatment

If you or a young person you know is struggling with drug addiction, it's important to seek professional help as soon as possible. Here are some steps you can take to seek treatment for drug addiction:

1. **Talk to a healthcare professional:** The first step in seeking treatment for drug addiction is to talk to a healthcare professional, such as a doctor, counselor, or addiction specialist. They can provide a professional assessment and recommend appropriate treatment options.
2. **Look for addiction treatment centers:** Addiction treatment centers offer a range of services, including detox, therapy, and medication-assisted treatment. You can search for addiction treatment centers in your area and find one that is tailored to your needs and preferences.

3. **Attend support groups:** Support groups, such as Alcoholics Anonymous (AA) or Narcotics Anonymous (NA), can provide valuable support and encouragement during the recovery process. Many support groups are available online or in person and are free to attend.
4. **Consider inpatient or outpatient treatment:** Inpatient treatment involves staying at a facility for a period of time to receive intensive treatment, while outpatient treatment involves attending treatment sessions while still living at home. The type of treatment you choose will depend on the severity of your addiction and your personal preferences.

Remember, seeking treatment for drug addiction can be challenging, but it's an important step in taking control of your life and your health. By seeking professional help and taking advantage of the resources available to you, you can overcome addiction and achieve lasting recovery.

As a parent, it can be difficult to see your child struggle with drug addiction. However, there are several ways you can help and support them through the process of seeking treatment and recovery:

1. **Be supportive and non-judgmental:** It's important to create a safe and supportive environment for your child to talk about their addiction and seek help. Let them know that you are there for them and that you support their decision to seek treatment.

2. **Educate yourself about addiction:** It's important to educate yourself about addiction, including the signs and symptoms of drug use and addiction, and the different types of treatment available. This can help you better understand what your child is going through and how you can support them in their recovery.
3. **Help them find treatment resources:** You can help your child find treatment resources, such as addiction treatment centers and support groups, and provide them with transportation to appointments and meetings.
4. **Attend therapy or support groups together:** Attending therapy or support groups together can help you and your child better understand each other's perspectives and provide additional support and encouragement.
5. **Encourage healthy habits:** Encourage your child to practice healthy habits, such as eating well, exercising, and getting enough sleep, which can support their overall physical and mental health.

Remember, addiction is a complex and challenging issue, and recovery is a process that takes time and effort. By being supportive, educated, and encouraging healthy habits, you can help your child navigate the process of seeking treatment and achieve lasting recovery.

Going through drug treatment can be a challenging and difficult process for both the child and the parent. As a parent, there are several ways you can support your child during this time:

1. **Be there for them:** It's important to be there for your child, both emotionally and physically. Attend therapy or support group sessions with them, provide transportation to appointments, and be available to listen and offer encouragement.
2. **Encourage and celebrate milestones:** Recovery is a process, and it's important to celebrate your child's progress and milestones along the way. Encourage them to keep going and remind them how proud you are of their efforts.
3. **Provide a stable and supportive environment:** Providing a stable and supportive home environment can help your child feel safe and supported during the recovery process. This can include providing healthy meals, establishing routines, and avoiding triggers and negative influences.
4. **Encourage healthy habits:** Encourage your child to practice healthy habits, such as exercise, meditation, and relaxation techniques, which can help them manage stress and support their overall physical and mental health.
5. **Practice self-care:** Taking care of yourself is also important when supporting a child through drug treatment. This can include seeking support from friends and family, practicing self-care activities, and engaging in activities that you enjoy.

Remember, supporting a child through drug treatment is a process that takes time, patience, and effort. By being there for your child, celebrating their milestones, providing a supportive environment, encouraging healthy habits, and practicing self-care, you can help your child navigate the recovery process and achieve lasting success.

Narcan

Narcan (also known as naloxone) is a medication used to reverse the effects of an opioid overdose. It works by quickly binding to the same receptors in the brain that opioids bind to, reversing their effects and restoring breathing.

If a person is experiencing an opioid overdose, administering Narcan can be a life-saving intervention. Narcan is available in several forms, including a nasal spray and an injectable solution.

For parents, it's important to be aware of Narcan and its availability, especially if they have a child who is at risk of an opioid overdose. Narcan can be obtained without a prescription at many pharmacies, and some states offer free Narcan programs for people who are at risk of overdose.

It's also important to know how to administer Narcan and what to do in the event of an opioid overdose. If you suspect that someone is experiencing an opioid overdose, call 911 immediately and administer Narcan if it is available.

While Narcan can be a life-saving intervention, it's important to remember that it is not a substitute for addiction treatment or other forms of professional help. If your child is struggling with opioid addiction, it's important to seek professional help from a healthcare provider or addiction specialist to address the underlying issue and support their recovery.

As a parent, it's important to keep Narcan (naloxone) handy if you have a child who is at risk of an opioid overdose. Narcan is a medication used to reverse the effects of an opioid overdose, and it can be a life-saving intervention in the event of an overdose.

It's also important to make sure your child knows how to use Narcan and has it readily available in case of an overdose. Educating your child about the risks of opioid use and the importance of having Narcan on hand can help empower them to take responsibility for their own safety and well-being.

By keeping Narcan on hand and educating your child about its importance, you can help reduce the risk of an opioid overdose and support their overall health and well-being.

Make the Move

As a youth advocate and mentor who has personally experienced the devastating effects of drug addiction and overdose, I cannot stress enough the importance of early intervention. We cannot afford to be complacent or naive when it comes to the dangers of Fentanyl and other drugs. We must be proactive in educating ourselves and our youth, recognizing the signs of addiction, and seeking help when needed. We must also approach addiction with compassion and understanding, recognizing that it is a complex issue with no easy solutions. With the right support and intervention, however, we can help our youth break the cycle of addiction and lead healthy, fulfilling lives.

What Parents Need to Know

Please do not be the parent who says:

- "My child is too innocent to be involved in drugs."
- "My child is in the church and would never do drugs or be around people who do them."
- "We live in a great neighborhood and my child goes to a great school and they will never do drugs."
- "We don't do drugs in this family."
- "Only poor kids do drugs, and my kids have everything they could ever want."
- "Only rich kids use pills, cocaine, and Fentanyl. My kids would never."

Wake up, parents! Don't be naive to think that your child is immune to drug addiction. The harsh reality is that no one is safe from the epidemic of Fentanyl and other drugs. Your child's innocence, church attendance, neighborhood, or socio-economic status is no guarantee of protection. Believing in these false assumptions could leave your child in danger of falling victim to addiction. With Fentanyl deaths on the rise, it's crucial to take action and educate our youth about the dangers of these substances. Don't bury your head in the sand, be proactive in keeping your child informed about the risks of drugs. Your decision to do so could very well save their life.

Signs

As a parent, it's important to be aware of the signs and symptoms of drug use, including Fentanyl use. Here are some common signs to look out for:

1. **Physical signs:** Fentanyl use can cause physical symptoms, such as constricted pupils, drowsiness, slowed breathing, and slurred speech.
2. **Behavioral changes:** If your child is using drugs, you may notice changes in their behavior, such as social withdrawal, changes in sleeping patterns, and sudden changes in mood or personality.
3. **Poor academic or work performance:** If your child's grades or work performance suddenly decline, it may be a sign of drug use.
4. **Secretive behavior:** If your child is suddenly secretive about their activities or whereabouts, it may be a sign that they are hiding drug use.
5. **Changes in appearance:** Drug use can sometimes lead to changes in appearance, such as sudden weight loss, neglecting personal hygiene, or track marks on the skin.

It's important to remember that these signs do not necessarily indicate drug use, and many of them can be caused by other factors as well. However, if you are concerned that your child may be using drugs, it's important to talk to them about your concerns and seek professional help if necessary.

Conversations

If a parent suspects that their child is using drugs, including Fentanyl, it's important to have a conversation as soon as possible. Delaying the conversation can increase the risk of harm or addiction, and it's important to address the issue before it escalates.

The conversation should be approached in a non-judgmental and supportive way, focusing on the child's health and well-being. It's important to listen to the child's perspective and to avoid blaming or shaming them for their behavior.

If the child denies using drugs, it's important to continue to monitor their behavior and to seek professional help if necessary. If the child admits to using drugs, it's important to provide support and encouragement for seeking professional help and treatment.

Remember, having a conversation about drugs can be difficult and emotional, but it's an important step in keeping your child safe and healthy. By being open and supportive, you can help your child navigate the complex issues surrounding drug use and seek the help they need to achieve lasting recovery.

Intervention

There are several intervention strategies and tactics that parents can use when they suspect that their child is addicted to drugs:

1. **Open communication:** Encourage open and honest communication with your child. Let them know that you are there to support them and help them through their struggles.
2. **Seek professional help:** Reach out to a professional such as a therapist, counselor, or addiction specialist who can help assess the situation and provide guidance on how to proceed.
3. **Support groups:** Find a support group for parents of addicted children, as this can be a helpful source of information, resources, and emotional support.
4. **Set boundaries and consequences:** Establish clear boundaries and consequences for drug use. This may include consequences such as limiting access to privileges or seeking professional help.
5. **Offer alternatives:** Encourage your child to engage in healthy activities that can replace drug use. This may include exercise, hobbies, or social activities that can help build positive relationships.
6. **Get involved:** Be involved in your child's life, including their friends and activities. This can help you identify any warning signs of drug use and provide the support they need.

It's important to note that every situation is unique, and there may be other intervention strategies and tactics that may be more effective for your child's situation. Seek the guidance of a professional for tailored advice and support.

What Schools Need to Know

I am continually amazed by the intelligence of young people. As my team and I have taught classes of 11-year-olds and younger, we've discovered that many of them are already aware of the effects of drugs and may even have family members struggling with addiction. Unfortunately, these children often don't feel comfortable sharing their struggles with teachers or counselors, which can lead to poor behavior and disinterest in schoolwork. As someone who experienced homelessness and a drug-affected home as a child, I know firsthand how difficult it is to share these problems with others. I was never asked if I was okay or if I had any issues at home by school staff, which only compounded my behavioral issues. It's important that we recognize and support young people who may be struggling at home and provide a safe and nurturing environment for them to thrive.

Signs

Teachers and other school staff can play an important role in identifying potential drug use among students, including Fentanyl use. Here are some signs that they can look out for:

1. **Changes in academic performance:** If a student's grades suddenly decline, it may be a sign of drug use.
2. **Changes in behavior:** If a student suddenly becomes withdrawn, apathetic, or disinterested in activities they previously enjoyed, it may be a sign of drug use.

3. **Changes in appearance:** Drug use can sometimes lead to changes in appearance, such as sudden weight loss, neglecting personal hygiene, or track marks on the skin.
4. **Excessive absences or tardiness:** If a student is frequently absent or tardy, it may be a sign of drug use.
5. **Mood changes:** If a student experiences sudden mood swings, aggressive behavior, or depression, it may be a sign of drug use.

It's important to remember that these signs do not necessarily indicate drug use, and many of them can be caused by other factors as well. However, if school staff are concerned that a student may be using drugs, it's important to approach the student in a supportive and non-judgmental way and to seek professional help if necessary.

Remember, early intervention is key to addressing drug use and preventing further harm or addiction. By being aware of the signs of drug use and providing support and resources for students who may be struggling, school staff can play an important role in promoting the health and well-being of their students.

How to Address Their Students

If teachers and school staff believe that a student may be using drugs, it's important to approach the situation with sensitivity, empathy, and support. Here are some steps that teachers and school staff can take to address their students:

1. **Express concern:** Approach the student in a private and non-judgmental way and express concern for their well-being. Let the student know that you are there to help and support them.
2. **Ask questions:** Ask the student if they are using drugs and if they need help. Encourage them to be honest and open about their situation.
3. **Provide resources:** If the student admits to drug use, provide them with information about resources and support services that can help, such as substance abuse treatment programs, counseling services, and support groups.
4. **Involve parents or guardians:** It's important to involve the student's parents or guardians in the conversation and to work together to provide support and resources for the student.
5. **Follow school policy:** Follow the school's policy on drug use and disciplinary action but prioritize the student's health and well-being in your approach.

Remember, addressing drug use among students can be a sensitive and complex issue, but it's important to approach it with empathy, support, and a focus on the student's health and well-being. By providing resources and support, teachers and school staff can play an important role in helping students who may be struggling with drug use.

How Can Schools Staff Intervene

If a student is known to be using drugs, it's important for school staff to intervene in a supportive and non-judgmental way to address the issue and provide resources and support for the student. Here are some steps that school staff can take to intervene:

1. **Meet with the student:** Meet with the student in a private and non-judgmental setting to express concern for their well-being and discuss their drug use.
2. **Involve parents or guardians:** Involve the student's parents or guardians in the conversation and work together to provide support and resources for the student.
3. **Provide resources:** Provide the student with information about resources and support services that can help, such as substance abuse treatment programs, counseling services, and support groups.
4. **Follow school policy:** Follow the school's policy on drug use and disciplinary action but prioritize the student's health and well-being in your approach.
5. **Monitor progress:** Monitor the student's progress and follow up regularly to ensure that they are receiving the support and resources they need.

It's important to remember that drug use is a complex issue, and addressing it requires a comprehensive and collaborative approach. By providing resources and support for students who are struggling with drug use, school staff can help promote the health and well-being of their students and prevent further harm or addiction.

What Should Schools Do

To inform their students and staff about the growing Fentanyl epidemic, schools can take several steps:

1. **Provide educational resources:** Schools can provide educational resources about Fentanyl and opioid use to both students and staff, such as brochures, posters, and classroom instruction. These resources can help raise awareness about the risks of drug use and the dangers of Fentanyl.
2. **Host guest speakers:** Schools can invite guest speakers, such as healthcare professionals or individuals in recovery, to share their experiences and insights about Fentanyl use. These presentations can help educate students and staff about the risks and consequences of drug use.
3. **Offer support services:** Schools can offer support services for students who may be struggling with drug use or mental health issues, such as counseling services or support groups. These services can provide students with the resources and support they need to make healthy choices and seek help when needed.

4. **Develop a crisis response plan:** Schools can develop a crisis response plan in the event of a drug overdose or other emergency related to drug use. This plan should include protocols for contacting emergency services, notifying parents or guardians, and providing support and resources for those affected.
5. **Engage with parents and community members:** Schools can engage with parents and community members to raise awareness about the Fentanyl epidemic and to promote community-wide efforts to prevent drug use and support recovery.

By taking these steps, schools can help educate their students and staff about the risks of Fentanyl and opioid use and provide resources and support for those who may be struggling with drug use.

It is important for schools to bring awareness to their students about Fentanyl and other drug use because education and awareness can help prevent drug abuse and related harms. According to the National Institute on Drug Abuse (NIDA), "Prevention programs that involve the family, schools, media, and communities are effective in reducing drug abuse." By educating students about the risks and consequences of drug use, schools can help prevent drug abuse and promote healthy decision-making.

Here is a statistic from the Centers for Disease Control and Prevention (CDC) to illustrate the importance of addressing Fentanyl use among students:

- From 2015 to 2017, the rate of drug overdose deaths involving synthetic opioids (including Fentanyl) increased by 84.2% among 15- to 24-year-olds in the United States.

This statistic highlights the growing prevalence of Fentanyl use and related harms among young people, making it especially important for schools to address this issue through education and prevention efforts.

Crisis Response Plan

A crisis response plan is important for schools to have in place because it helps ensure that students and staff are safe in the event of an emergency, such as a drug overdose or other drug-related incident. By having a clear plan in place, school staff can quickly and effectively respond to the situation, minimize harm, and provide support and resources for those affected.

In addition, having a crisis response plan can help reduce anxiety and uncertainty for students, parents, and staff. It provides a clear set of procedures and protocols for responding to emergencies, which can help instill a sense of confidence and security in the school community.

A crisis response plan can also help schools comply with legal and regulatory requirements for responding to emergencies. Schools are often required by law to have an emergency plan in place, and failure to do so can result in legal liability or other consequences.

Finally, a crisis response plan can help schools identify areas for improvement and take steps to prevent future emergencies. By evaluating the response to a crisis and identifying areas for improvement, schools can take proactive measures to prevent similar incidents from occurring in the future.

Overall, a crisis response plan is an essential tool for schools to ensure the safety and well-being of their students and staff in the event of an emergency.

Crisis Response Plan Example

Here is an example of what a crisis response plan for a drug overdose or other emergency related to drug use might include for a school:

1. **Contact emergency services:** In the event of a drug overdose or other drug-related emergency, school staff should immediately call 911 or the local emergency services number to request assistance. The staff member making the call should provide as much information as possible about the situation, including the location, the student's name, and any known information about the drugs involved.
2. **Notify parents or guardians:** Once emergency services have been contacted, the school should notify the student's parents or guardians about the situation. The school should provide as much information as

possible, while respecting the student's privacy.

3. **Provide support and resources:** In the aftermath of a drug-related emergency, the school should provide support and resources for all students and staff affected by the situation. This may include counseling services, support groups, or other resources to help students cope with the incident.

4. **Evaluate the situation:** After the immediate crisis has been addressed, the school should evaluate the situation to determine how it can improve its response in the future. This may involve reviewing the crisis response plan, providing additional training for staff, or implementing new policies to prevent drug use on campus.

By having a crisis response plan in place, schools can be better prepared to respond to drug-related emergencies and provide the support and resources that students and staff need to stay safe and healthy.

Bring Awareness to Your Students About Fentanyl

Schools should provide their students with Fentanyl awareness information because Fentanyl-related deaths have been increasing at an alarming rate in recent years, especially among young people. According to the Centers for Disease Control and Prevention (CDC), there was a 55% increase in Fentanyl-related overdose deaths among people aged 15-24 in 2019 compared to the previous year. This trend is expected to continue, as Fentanyl remains a major public health concern.

Furthermore, research has shown that education and prevention efforts are effective in reducing drug use among young people. The National Institute on Drug Abuse (NIDA) has found that school-based prevention programs can help to reduce drug use by as much as 50%. By providing Fentanyl awareness information to their students, schools can help to reduce the risk of Fentanyl-related harm and empower young people to make informed decisions about drug use.

In addition, schools have a duty to protect their students from harm and provide a safe and healthy learning environment. By educating their students about the dangers of Fentanyl, schools can fulfill this responsibility and help to prevent drug-related harm and tragedies.

Utilize Lived Experience Experts

Utilizing people with Lived Experience to speak to students about drugs and Fentanyl can be highly beneficial for several reasons. First, individuals with Lived Experience can offer a unique and relatable perspective to students. By sharing their own stories of addiction and recovery, they can help students understand the real-life consequences of drug use and the challenges of overcoming addiction.

Additionally, Lived Experience experts can provide students with information and insights that may not be available from traditional sources such as textbooks or lectures. They can speak directly to the emotional and psychological aspects of drug use and addiction and can offer practical advice on how to avoid the dangers of drugs like Fentanyl.

Studies have shown that using Lived Experience experts in drug education programs can be highly effective in reducing drug use among youth. For example, a study published in the Journal of Adolescent Health found that a drug education program that utilized peer mentors with Lived Experience was significantly more effective in reducing drug use among high school students than traditional drug education programs.

Overall, utilizing Lived Experience experts in drug education programs can help students understand the real dangers of drug use, provide practical advice on how to avoid addiction, and reduce the incidence of drug use among youth.

Legal Consequences

Based on my lived experience as someone who was once involved in drug use and sales, I can say with certainty that people from all walks of life, regardless of their social or economic status, both consume and sell drugs. Despite the societal notion that only those from lower-income neighborhoods engage in such activities, I have witnessed kids from prestigious universities and private religious high schools involved in drug use and sales as well.

In this guidebook, I strive to provide truthful and honest information. As someone who has worked in youth advocacy and training, I have come to realize that the best way to warn and stop those who profit financially from illegal activities is to inform them of the legal consequences of their actions. Often, individuals who engage in such activities are unaware of the legal repercussions until they are charged with a crime and standing in front of a judge.

Warning Warning!

Distributing Fentanyl on the streets is illegal and can result in serious legal consequences. In the United States, Fentanyl is classified as a Schedule II controlled substance under the Controlled Substances Act, which means that it has a high potential for abuse and may lead to severe psychological or physical dependence.

Individuals who distribute Fentanyl on the streets may face criminal charges, including possession with intent to distribute, drug trafficking, and manufacturing or distributing a controlled substance. These charges can result in severe penalties, including significant fines, imprisonment, and a criminal record that can have lasting consequences.

In addition to criminal charges, individuals who distribute Fentanyl on the streets may also face civil liability for any harm caused by their actions. This can include civil lawsuits brought by individuals who have suffered harm as a result of Fentanyl use, as well as fines and other penalties imposed by regulatory agencies.

Overall, the legal consequences of distributing Fentanyl on the streets can be severe and long-lasting. It is important for individuals to understand the risks of this illegal activity and to seek help if they are struggling with addiction or other related issues.

My Mentee's Story

My mentee, Michael Steen (aka "Yung Poppy"), was a young individual with a heart of gold and a natural talent for making people smile and laugh. When he was just 17 years old, he started working with me as a promoter for my concert promoting business. As social media started to gain popularity, he became one of the first major social media influencers, gaining a following of over 2 million on platforms such as Vine, Instagram, and YouTube with his short sketch comedies and entertaining spirit.

Many, including myself, were unaware that Michael was struggling with drug and pharmaceutical addiction. He started using drugs at the young age of 15. As his social media career grew and he began earning more income as an influencer, he fell deeper into addiction and consumed more drugs. In 2018, Yung Poppy unknowingly supplied a Fentanyl-laced pill to a friend who subsequently passed away. Unfortunately, he had also been consuming these pills himself. After his friend's death, Yung Poppy sold drugs to an undercover officer and was later linked to his friend's overdose. During his court proceedings, he suffered from two drug overdoses and nearly lost his life. In 2020, he was sentenced to 12 years and 4 months in federal prison where he currently remains.

My young friend is filled with remorse for his past actions and constantly urges me to spread awareness about the dangers of the deadly drug Fentanyl. Despite being in prison, he has initiated a movement called the "Stop Fentanyl Project" and wishes to use his story to help others from falling victim to the drug. With his remaining celebrity reach of over 1.6 million followers on Instagram, I hope to get him out in the world again to use his voice and influence to reach out to masses of people.

In conclusion, whether a person is using or selling Fentanyl, there is no winner. The consequences can be devastating and life-changing, affecting not only the individual but also their loved ones and the wider community. By raising awareness and having open conversations about the dangers of Fentanyl, we can help prevent more tragedies and potentially save lives. It is up to all of us to come together and take action in the fight against this deadly epidemic.

Yung Poppy's Statement From Federal Prison

My message for those who use and sell Fentanyl is this: Look at what happened to me, Yung Poppy, a social media icon with a lot going for me. Ask yourself, is Fentanyl worth losing everything over? Drug use leads to bad things like homelessness, incarceration, and/or death. Is it worth any of those three? I don't think so. Fentanyl is the deadliest drug out there right now, killing people with no second chance. It's more addictive not just to users but to dealers who make so much money because of how addictive it is. It's sad.

I was addicted to Fentanyl, and I know exactly what comes of it—tragedy. Users, care more about yourself and the people you love. Clean yourself up before it's too late. Recently, I lost a friend, Petey. He was only 18 years old and lost his life to this drug. That broke me to pieces. To the dealers—come on! Life in prison is not worth a few dollars. What you are doing isn't right, and people are dying. That should be enough right there. Think about if it was your family member before selling to somebody, especially an underage child.

— Michael "Yung Poppy" Steen, founder or the Stop Fentanyl Project

Understanding the Fight Ahead

With over a decade of experience in community service and non-profit work, I have created and led numerous youth mentorship programs. However, during this time, I have come to realize the significant challenges presented by the outside world, which often contradicted the positive messages I was trying to impart to these young people. Despite dedicating only an hour each week to mentorship, I strived to offer as much love and positive guidance as possible. Nevertheless, upon leaving our sessions, many of these youths returned to environments that were filled with negative influences, toxic family dynamics, and friends who were not receiving any form of mentorship or support. It was often discouraging, and at times it felt like an impossible war to win. Nevertheless, we continued to plant seeds of positivity, much like a farmer, because the fight to help our youth was worth it.

The Music Industry and Pop Culture

The promotion of pharmaceutical pills in pop culture and music is a complex issue that has been a topic of debate for many years. While some argue that the promotion of pharmaceutical pills in pop culture and music can help to raise awareness about certain medical conditions and treatments, others are concerned that it can contribute to the over-prescription of medications and the misuse of prescription drugs.

In some cases, pharmaceutical companies may pay celebrities or music artists to promote their products, or they may provide samples or other incentives to healthcare providers to encourage them to prescribe their drugs. These marketing tactics can help to increase sales of pharmaceutical products, but they can also contribute to the overuse or misuse of these drugs.

In music, there are numerous examples of lyrics that reference the use of prescription drugs, including painkillers, tranquilizers, and stimulants. Some artists have even been criticized for glorifying the use of drugs in their music or promoting the misuse of prescription medications.

The promotion of pharmaceutical pills in pop culture and music can also have an impact on public perceptions of these drugs. Some people may be more likely to seek out prescription medications based on the recommendations of celebrities or popular media, without fully understanding the risks associated with these drugs.

It's important to note that prescription medications can be effective treatments for many medical conditions, and they can help to improve the quality of life for many people. However, it's also important to use these drugs responsibly and to be aware of the potential for misuse and addiction. Healthcare providers and pharmaceutical companies have a responsibility to promote the appropriate use of medications and to provide accurate information about the risks and benefits of these drugs.

Social Media

Social media has been used as a platform to promote the use of opioids and other pharmaceuticals in several ways. Here are some examples:

1. **Paid advertising:** Pharmaceutical companies may pay to advertise their products on social media, targeting specific audiences with sponsored posts or ads. These ads can make the drugs seem appealing and downplay the risks associated with their use.
2. **Influencer marketing:** Similar to other products, pharmaceutical companies may collaborate with influencers or celebrities to promote their products on social media. Influencers may post photos, videos, or other content featuring the drugs or discussing their benefits and may receive compensation for doing so.
3. **Information sharing:** Social media can be used to share information about prescription drugs and their benefits, making them seem more desirable or necessary. Users may see posts from friends or family members talking about their positive experiences with a certain drug or may find information online that suggests the drug is effective and safe.
4. **Peer pressure:** Social media can create a sense of peer pressure to use prescription drugs, as users may feel compelled to fit in with their social group or keep up with trends and influencers on the platform.

5. **Misinformation:** Social media can also spread misinformation about prescription drugs, with users sharing inaccurate information about the effects, risks, and benefits of these drugs.

It's important to note that prescription medications can be effective treatments for many medical conditions, and they can help to improve the quality of life for many people. However, it's also important to use these drugs responsibly and to be aware of the potential for misuse, addiction, and overdose. Healthcare providers and pharmaceutical companies have a responsibility to promote the appropriate use of medications and to provide accurate information about the risks and benefits of these drugs. Social media platforms also have a responsibility to monitor and remove drug-related content, and to ensure that users are not engaging in illegal activities on their platforms.

Celebrity Deaths

When I give presentations in schools to raise awareness about Fentanyl, I often use examples of celebrities. Many high-profile celebrities have lost their lives due to Fentanyl overdoses in recent years, and one of the most prominent examples I discuss with young people is Logan Williams. The coroner's report on his death confirmed that the 16-year-old actor passed away on April 2, 2020, due to an accidental drug overdose that involved Fentanyl. Williams, who was born in Coquitlam, British Columbia, was best known for his role as the young Barry Allen in The CW's The Flash, which is frequently filmed in Burnaby. He also had minor roles in other TV series, such as Supernatural and When Calls the Heart.

Using the example of high-profile celebrities who have died from Fentanyl overdoses, such as young actor Logan Williams, can be an effective way to grab the attention of youth when discussing the dangers of Fentanyl. By highlighting the tragic loss of a well-known and beloved celebrity, youth may be more likely to pay attention and take the issue seriously. Additionally, many youth are active on social media and may follow these celebrities or be influenced by their actions. Using these examples can help to make the dangers of Fentanyl more real and relatable to the youth and may motivate them to make better choices to avoid falling victim to addiction and overdose.

Here are a few other examples:

1. **Prince:** The musician Prince died in 2016 due to an accidental Fentanyl overdose. He was found unresponsive in an elevator at his home and later pronounced dead at the age of 57.
2. **Tom Petty:** The musician Tom Petty died in 2017 due to an accidental overdose of several drugs, including Fentanyl. He had been prescribed the drug for pain management.
3. **Mac Miller:** The rapper Mac Miller died in 2018 due to an accidental overdose of Fentanyl, cocaine, and alcohol. He was 26 years old.
4. **Lil Peep:** The rapper Lil Peep died in 2017 due to an accidental overdose of Fentanyl and Xanax. He was 21 years old.

5. **DMX:** The rapper DMX died in 2021 due to a heart attack, which was complicated by a drug overdose that included Fentanyl.
6. **Lauren Braxton:** Niece of R&B pop star Toni Braxton died in 2019 of a heroin overdose and Fentanyl intoxication. She was 24.
7. **Tytyana Miller:** Actress and daughter of rapper Master P died in 2022 at 29 of accidental Fentanyl intoxication.

These deaths have brought increased attention to the dangers of Fentanyl and the importance of preventing opioid addiction and overdose. It's important to seek help if you or someone you know is struggling with substance use, and to be aware of the risks associated with these powerful drugs.

What Can I Do?

As someone who has survived overdosing, drug addiction, and lost many friends to Fentanyl, I urge parents and school staff to take action to help prevent our youth from falling victim to addiction. The dangers of Fentanyl are real, and it is critical that we educate and provide support for our young people.

Fentanyl is a highly potent and deadly drug, and even a small amount can cause an overdose. It is being found in various drugs, including pills, heroin, and cocaine, making it difficult for users to know what they are consuming. We cannot rely on our youth to protect themselves from the dangers of Fentanyl. As parents and educators, it is our responsibility to help them understand the risks and to provide them with the tools and resources they need to stay safe.

Parents

There are several tangible steps that parents can take to help fight the Fentanyl epidemic in their home. Here are a few examples:

1. **Secure medications:** Parents can take steps to secure their prescription medications and keep them out of reach of children and teens. This can include locking up medications or keeping them in a secure location.
2. **Monitor medication use:** Parents can also monitor their own medication use and that of their children, keeping track of when medications are taken and how many pills are

left. This can help to identify potential misuse or diversion of medication.

3. **Educate children:** Parents can talk to their children about the risks of Fentanyl and other drugs, including the dangers of using drugs that are obtained from unknown sources. Education can also include teaching children about the signs of an overdose and how to respond in an emergency.

4. **Have naloxone on hand:** Parents can obtain naloxone, a medication that can reverse the effects of an opioid overdose and keep it on hand in case of an emergency. This can be obtained through a healthcare provider or a pharmacy.

5. **Seek treatment:** If a family member is struggling with addiction, it's important to seek treatment and support. This can include contacting a healthcare provider, a substance abuse treatment center, or a support group for families affected by addiction.

These are just a few examples of tangible steps that parents can take to help fight the Fentanyl epidemic in their home. It's important to stay informed about the risks associated with Fentanyl and other drugs, and to take steps to prevent misuse and overdose.

School Staff

There are several tangible steps that school staff can take to help fight the Fentanyl epidemic in their school. Here are a few examples:

1. **Educate students:** School staff can provide education to students about the risks of Fentanyl and other drugs, including the dangers of using drugs obtained from unknown sources. This can include classroom lessons, school-wide presentations, and other educational resources.
2. **Create a crisis response plan:** School staff can work together to create a crisis response plan in the event of a drug overdose or other emergency related to drug use. This plan can include protocols for contacting emergency services, notifying parents or guardians, and providing support and resources for those affected.
3. **Provide resources and support:** School staff can provide resources and support to students and families affected by addiction. This can include connecting families with community resources, providing counseling or mental health services, and offering support groups for students and families affected by addiction.
4. **Monitor for signs of drug use:** School staff can monitor for signs of drug use among students, including changes in behavior, physical symptoms, and academic performance. Staff can also be trained to identify and respond to potential drug overdoses.
5. **Advocate for policy change:** School staff can advocate for policy change to help prevent addiction and overdose, such as supporting programs that provide medication-assisted treatment for addiction and promoting policies that limit the over-prescription of opioids.

These are just a few examples of tangible steps that school staff can take to help fight the Fentanyl epidemic in their school. It's important for school staff to work together and take a proactive approach to preventing addiction and overdose among students.

We Can Do This Together

The consequences of not taking action are severe. We are losing young people to Fentanyl overdose at an alarming rate. These are people who had their entire lives ahead of them and so much potential. We cannot afford to lose any more. We need to be proactive and engage our youth in conversations about drugs, addiction, and the consequences that come with them.

By taking a proactive approach, we can help our youth avoid the dangers of Fentanyl and drug addiction. We need to teach them the warning signs of drug use and provide them with resources and support if they or someone they know is struggling. It is important to create a safe and non-judgmental space where youth can feel comfortable discussing any problems they may be experiencing.

Parents and school staff need to work together to make a difference in the lives of our youth. We can all play a role in educating and protecting our young people. Let us all take a stand against the Fentanyl epidemic and fight to protect our future generation.

Getting Help

When it comes to raising awareness, prevention, and intervention strategies related to Fentanyl, parents and school staff have an important role to play in protecting youth from this deadly drug. It's crucial to equip youth with the knowledge and tools they need to make informed decisions and to recognize the warning signs of Fentanyl addiction. One effective way to do this is by enlisting the help of lived experience experts who can provide firsthand knowledge and relatable experiences to connect with and engage youth. In this guidebook section, we'll explore the benefits of utilizing lived experience experts in Fentanyl prevention efforts and provide practical tips for parents and school staff on how to get the help they need to protect their youth.

If a parent is concerned that their child has a drug addiction, there are several steps they can take to get help. Here are a few examples:

1. **Talk to a healthcare provider:** The first step in getting help for a child's drug addiction is to talk to a healthcare provider, such as a primary care physician, a pediatrician, or a mental health professional. They can provide an assessment of the child's needs and make recommendations for treatment.
2. **Find a substance abuse treatment program:** There are many substance abuse treatment programs available, including inpatient and outpatient programs, group therapy, and individual counseling. Parents can research

local programs and work with their healthcare provider to identify the most appropriate treatment option.

3. **Join a support group:** Parents can find support and resources by joining a support group for families affected by addiction. These groups can provide information, education, and emotional support.

4. **Create a plan for ongoing care:** Recovery from addiction is a long-term process, and it's important for parents to create a plan for ongoing care and support. This can include regular check-ins with healthcare providers, participation in support groups, and ongoing communication with the child about their recovery.

5. **Consider medication-assisted treatment:** In some cases, medication-assisted treatment (MAT) may be appropriate for treating a child's addiction. MAT combines medication with counseling and other support to help manage cravings and withdrawal symptoms.

6. **Utilize lived experience:** A parent can utilize lived experience experts and organizations run by them to bring awareness and intervention from Fentanyl by seeking out individuals who have first-hand experience with drug addiction and recovery. These experts can provide valuable insights and perspectives that can help parents understand the risks associated with drug use, the signs of addiction, and the best ways to intervene when they suspect that their child may be at risk. By working with lived experience experts, parents can access a

wealth of knowledge and expertise that can help them better protect their children from the dangers of Fentanyl and other drugs.

These are just a few examples of steps that parents can take to get help for a child's drug addiction. It's important to remember that addiction is a treatable condition, and that there are resources available to help families through the recovery process.

If a school staff member is concerned that a student has a drug addiction, there are several steps they can take to get help. Here are a few examples:

1. **Contact the student's parents or guardians:** It's important to involve the student's parents or guardians in the process of getting help for a drug addiction. School staff can work with parents to identify appropriate resources for treatment and support.
2. **Provide resources and support:** Schools can provide resources and support to students and families affected by addiction, including counseling, mental health services, and support groups. School staff can work with community organizations and healthcare providers to identify local resources.
3. **Develop a student-specific treatment plan:** School staff can work with healthcare providers and families to develop a student-specific treatment plan, which can include counseling, medication-assisted treatment, and other forms of therapy. This plan can also

include academic and social support to help the student continue their education while in treatment.

4. **Ensure student safety:** It's important for school staff to prioritize student safety and well-being. In the event of a drug overdose or other emergency related to drug use, school staff should follow the crisis response plan and contact emergency services as needed.

5. **Advocate for policy change:** School staff can advocate for policy change to help prevent addiction and overdose, such as supporting programs that provide medication-assisted treatment for addiction and promoting policies that limit the over-prescription of opioids.

6. **Utilize lived experience:** Schools can play a critical role in educating students about the dangers of Fentanyl and preventing the devastating consequences of drug addiction. One effective way to do this is by utilizing lived experience experts who can share their personal stories and insights to bring awareness and intervention from Fentanyl. By incorporating lived experience experts into awareness assemblies and presentations, schools can provide a unique perspective and powerful message that can resonate with students and inspire them to make positive choices. These experts can not only educate students about the dangers of Fentanyl but also provide resources and support for those who may be struggling with addiction or have loved ones impacted by drug use.

These are just a few examples of steps that schools can take to get help for a student's drug addiction. It's important for school staff to work together and take a proactive approach to preventing addiction and overdose among students.

Educate Educate Educate

Educating our youth about Fentanyl is crucial because Fentanyl is a highly potent synthetic opioid that has contributed to a significant increase in drug overdoses and deaths in recent years. Fentanyl is often added to other drugs, such as heroin, cocaine, and counterfeit prescription pills, without the user's knowledge. As a result, users are at a higher risk of overdose, and even a small amount of Fentanyl can be deadly.

Educating youth about the risks of Fentanyl use can help prevent addiction and overdose. This includes providing information about the dangers of using drugs obtained from unknown sources and teaching young people how to recognize the signs of a potential overdose. Educating youth about Fentanyl can also help to reduce the stigma surrounding addiction and promote healthy behaviors.

In addition to prevention, educating youth about Fentanyl can also be important in the event of an overdose. Young people who are educated about the risks of Fentanyl use may be more likely to call for help in the event of an overdose and provide potentially life-saving interventions, such as administering naloxone (Narcan), a medication that can reverse the effects of an opioid overdose.

Overall, educating our youth about Fentanyl is critical to preventing addiction and overdose and promoting healthy behaviors. By providing young people with the information they need to make informed decisions about drug use, we can help to reduce the impact of the Fentanyl epidemic and save lives.

There are several resources available for parents and schools to find Lived Experience Experts who can help educate their youth about Fentanyl and drug use. One option is to reach out to local community organizations and nonprofits that specialize in drug prevention and education. These organizations may have a network of Lived Experience Experts who are willing to share their stories and provide support. Another option is to contact local substance abuse treatment centers or support groups, as they may also have Lived Experience Experts who are available to speak to parents and students. Additionally, there are online directories and databases of speakers and advocates with lived experience that can be found with a simple search.

In addition to seeking out resources from community organizations and local agencies, parents and schools can also receive assistance with awareness, prevention, and intervention from our Walk With Me Impact team of lived experience experts and youth consultants. Our team is dedicated to providing the most up-to-date information and practical strategies for helping youth stay safe and avoid the dangers of Fentanyl. With our firsthand experience and expertise, we can help bridge the gap between youth and adults and create a more informed and empowered community.

As a youth advocate who has lost nearly two dozen friends to overdose in just the past two years, I cannot emphasize enough the urgency of taking action to combat the Fentanyl epidemic. We cannot afford to sit idly by and hope that the problem will simply go away. It is critical that parents and schools take proactive measures to educate and protect our youth, and utilizing lived experience experts can make a significant impact. Please, do not wait until it's too late. The time to act is now.

Walk With Me Impact (WWMI) Youth Mentoring Curriculum

Our mission is to empower youth by providing mentorship and education that foster self-awareness and core values, ultimately leading to the development of strong community members, leaders, and families. We are dedicated to saving the lives of our youth and strive to make a worldwide impact.

The WWMI youth mentoring curriculum is a 3-book set designed to provide targeted prevention curriculum for youth and support for mentors. The curriculum features audio and visual aids, which will enhance the messaging delivered by Lived Experience Experts.

In-School Presentations

We utilize the concepts from the WWMI curriculum to assist in providing in- school presentations to students. As our outreach increased, we confirmed that having a presence in schools is beneficial as many of the youth are unaware of the dangers of Fentanyl and the fact that just one pill can be fatal. This highlights the importance of avoiding drugs altogether.

Additional Training and Services

Our curriculum is available for youth programs, juvenile detention facilities, parents, mentors, schools, and any individual looking to support youth. As an additional support we offer training services to help mentors address the many toxic issues affecting youth.

- Fentanyl Awareness
- Mentorship Development
- Gun Violence
- Staff Development
- Human Sex Trafficking
- Restorative Practice Training
- Community Outreach
- Trauma Informed Care Training
- Community Awareness Presentations
- Substance Abuse
- Youth Gang Involvement
- Youth Consultants

Contact Us

Phone: (858)-997-7690
Email: info@wwmimpact.com
Address: 3960 W. Point Loma Blvd., Ste. H-343
San Diego, CA 92110

In Memory and Dedication of My Loved Ones Lost

We will never forget the loved ones we have lost to drug-related issues and Fentanyl, their memory will live on in our hearts. To honor their lives and keep their memory alive, I dedicate this book to them. Let us always remember their beautiful souls and the impact they had on our lives and use their memories as motivation to continue the fight against this deadly epidemic and help this message save lives.

Rest peacefully, loved ones.

Mothers' Messages

My son Elijah ordered what he thought were 15 pain pills from a guy that was recommended to him. Based on conversations between Elijah and his death dealer, my son seemed to trust him. After several weeks of going back and forth, he placed an order.

The morning that his grandma found him dead, 14 blue pills stamped with an M 30 were found. We believe that he took one pill and that caused his death. Each pill recovered and tested contained a lethal dose of fentanyl. I'm beyond heartbroken, but still grateful Elijah didn't share any of those pills with people he knew.

Losing Elijah feels like my heart has been ripped out of my chest and I'm looking at it in front me. It aches constantly, but somehow still works. I pray that no one ever has to go through the deception and loss associated with illicit fentanyl use. As my friend Juli says, the truth is "one line, one pill—fentanyl kills."

Fentanyl changes everything. If you don't die, you're almost guaranteed to become addicted to something 50 times stronger than heroin. Please don't put your mother through this agonizing loss and devastation.

Your plug is not your homie, they don't care about you. To them, all you are is another dollar and collateral damage.

– Perla Mendoza

Website: www.projecteli.info
Instagram: elijahs.mama
Facebook: Project Eli

As a mother I can say that fentanyl and counterfeit drugs are my biggest fear. As much as I want to think that I educated and prepared my children for the dangers that those drugs pose, I do not think any of us can be completely sure that we have done enough in that regard. It is never enough.

The pressure our children are under nowadays cannot be compared to what we went through at their age. The expectation to succeed is often too much and the promise of extra energy and the ability to focus that some of these counterfeit drugs offer is often too much of a temptation to resist.

These pills often come from online sources, websites that promise prescription meds through online consultations. They often look like the real deal and even the pills that are shipped to the house look like the ones doctors would subscribe. And that is where the real danger lies.

Talk to your children. Often. Remind them not to buy pills online, not to buy them from friends or acquaintances and never to trust any medication given to them by anyone other than their doctor or pharmacist. It only takes one pill. One pill can kill.

— Alexandra Dionisio, founder and host of the Learning to Say Goodbye Podcast.

If you want to hear more about the subject tune in to episode 9 of season 1, available at all major podcast streaming services.

References

- Australian Bureau of Statistics

- Canadian Institute for Health Information

- *Journal of Adolescent Health*

- National Institute on Drug Abuse

- Office for National Statistics

- US Drug Enforcement Administration (DEA)

- World Drug Report 2021 published by the United Nations Office on Drugs and Crime (UNODC)

Made in the USA
Monee, IL
04 May 2023